WINNIE~THE~POOH

DEEP THOUGHTS & PONDERINGS FOR THE WISE

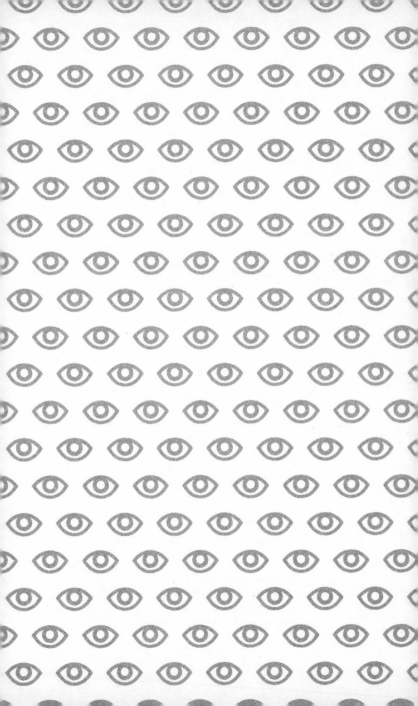

EGMONT

We bring stories to life

First published in 2018 by Egmont UK Limited
The Yellow Building, 1 Nicholas Road, London W11 4AN
www.egmont.co.uk

Additional text by Catherine Shoolbred
Designed by Pritty Ramjee

ISBN 978 1 4052 9196 5
68940/001
Printed in the UK

WINNIE~THE~POOH

DEEP THOUGHTS & PONDERINGS FOR THE WISE

A.A.MILNE
with decorations by **E.H.SHEPARD**

EGMONT

INTRODUCTION

'Rabbit's clever,' said Pooh thoughtfully.
'Yes,' said Piglet, 'Rabbit's clever.'
'And he has Brain.'
'Yes,' said Piglet, 'Rabbit has Brain.'
There was a long silence.
'I suppose,' said Pooh, 'that that's
why he never understands anything.'

He may be known as the Bear of Very Little Brain but, if you look beyond his muddles, there is true wisdom in Winnie~the~Pooh's words. So, no matter whether your intellect towers above all others or hides humbly away, this gently~humorous book is sure to make you that little bit wiser.

YOUR BRAIN MAY BE LARGE OR SMALL ...

'And if anyone knows anything about
anything,' said Bear to himself,
'it's Owl who knows something about
something,' he said, 'or my name's
not Winnie-the-Pooh,' he said.
'Which it is,' he added. 'So there you are.'

... BUT WHAT IS CERTAIN IS THAT YOU ARE FULL OF SURPRISES.

*Pooh ... said something so clever
that Christopher Robin could only look
at him with mouth open and eyes staring,
wondering if this was really the Bear
of Very Little Brain whom he had
known and loved so long.*

Even small brains can reach the right conclusion ...

'What I said was, "Is anybody at home?"'
called out Pooh very loudly.
'No!' said a voice; and then added,
'You needn't shout so loud.
I heard you quite well the first time.'
'Bother!' said Pooh. 'Isn't there anybody here at all?'
'Nobody.'
Winnie-the-Pooh took his head out of the hole,
and thought for a little, and he thought to
himself, 'There must be somebody there,
because somebody must have said "Nobody."'

... AND SMALL BRAINS SOMETIMES HAVE BIG IDEAS.

Pooh began to feel a little more comfortable, because when you are a Bear of Very Little Brain, and you Think of Things, you find sometimes that a Thing which seemed very Thingish inside you is quite different when it gets out into the open and has other people looking at it.

SOME FRIENDS APPRECIATE YOUR INTELLECT ...

'I see now,' said Winnie-the-Pooh.
'I have been Foolish and Deluded,' said he,
'and I am a Bear of No Brain at All.'
'You're the Best Bear in All the World,'
said Christopher Robin soothingly.
'Am I?' said Pooh hopefully.
And then he brightened up suddenly.
'Anyhow,' he said, 'it is nearly Luncheon Time.'
So he went home for it.

... BUT THEY WON'T ALL SEE THE VALUE OF EDUCATION.

But Eeyore was saying to himself, 'This writing business. Pencils and what-not. Over-rated, if you ask me. Silly stuff. Nothing in it.'

SOME WILL BE QUICK TO POINT OUT THE GAPS IN YOUR LEARNING …

'Do you know what A means, little Piglet?'
'No, Eeyore, I don't.'
'It means Learning, it means Education,
it means all the things that you and Pooh
haven't got. That's what A means.'

... EVEN IF STUDYING FRUSTRATES THEM.

'Clever!' said Eeyore scornfully,
putting a foot heavily on his three sticks.
'Education!' said Eeyore bitterly,
jumping on his six sticks.
'What is Learning?' asked Eeyore
as he kicked his twelve sticks into the air.
'A thing Rabbit knows! Ha!'

YOU ARE ONLY AS CLEVER AS WHAT YOU KNOW ...

For Owl, wise though he was in many ways,
able to read and write and spell his own
name WOL, yet somehow went
all to pieces over delicate words like
MEASLES and BUTTEREDTOAST.

... AND SOMETIMES YOU DON'T KNOW THAT MUCH.

And he respects Owl, because you can't help respecting anybody who can spell TUESDAY, even if he doesn't spell it right; but spelling isn't everything. There are days when spelling Tuesday simply doesn't count.

Spelling may not be
a skill that you possess ...

'Where are we going to on this Expotition?'
'Expedition, silly old Bear. It's got an "x" in it.'
'Oh!' said Pooh. 'I know.' But he didn't really.

... AND YOUR FRIENDS MIGHT FIND IT JUST AS HARD.

So Owl wrote ... and this is what he wrote:
HIP PAPY BTHUTHDTH
THUTHDA BTHUTHDY.
Pooh looked on admiringly.
'I'm just saying "A Happy Birthday,"'
said Owl carelessly.
'It's a nice long one,' said Pooh,
very much impressed by it.
'Well, actually, of course,

I'm saying "A Very Happy Birthday
with love from Pooh."
Naturally it takes a good deal
of pencil to say a long thing like that.'

YOU MAY STRUGGLE WITH MORE COMPLICATED WORDS ...

'Well,' said Owl,
'the customary procedure
in such cases is as follows.'
'What does Crustimoney
Proseedcake mean?' said Pooh.
'For I am a Bear of Very Little Brain,
and long words Bother me.'

... BUT YOU KNOW WHO TO ASK IF YOU NEED HELP.

'I must find Christopher Robin or Owl
or Piglet, one of those Clever Readers
who can read things, and they will
tell me what this missage means.
Only I can't swim. Bother!'

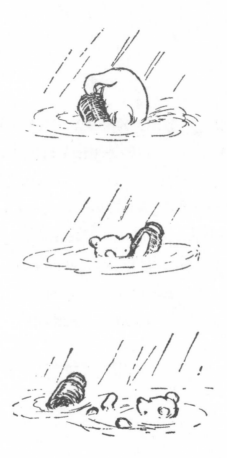

SOME PEOPLE USE FANCIER LANGUAGE THAN YOU.

'The atmospheric conditions have
been very unfavourable lately,' said Owl.
'The what?'
'It has been raining,' explained Owl.
'Yes,' said Christopher Robin. 'It has.'

YOU SAY POTATO
AND I SAY POTATO.

*'And we must all
bring Provisions.'
'Bring what?'
'Things to eat.'
'Oh!' said Pooh happily.
'I thought you
said Provisions.
I'll go and tell them.'*

SOMETIMES YOU STRUGGLE TO SAY WHAT YOU MEAN ...

Pooh knew what he meant,
but being a Bear of Very Little Brain,
couldn't think of the words.

... SO YOU'RE THANKFUL WHEN PEOPLE DON'T JUMP TO CONCLUSIONS.

'Pooh,' said Owl severely 'did you do that?'

'No,' said Pooh humbly. 'I don't think so.'

'Then who did?'

'I think it was the wind,' said Piglet.

'I think your house has blown down.'

'Oh, is that it? I thought it was Pooh.'

'No,' said Pooh.

'If it was the wind,' said Owl, considering

the matter, 'then it wasn't Pooh's fault.

No blame can be attached to him.'

YOU ALWAYS APPRECIATE A COMPLIMENT, EVEN IF YOU DON'T FULLY UNDERSTAND IT.

'Owl,' said Pooh, 'I have thought of something.'
'Astute and Helpful Bear,' said Owl.
Pooh looked proud at being called a stout
and helpful bear, and said modestly that
he just happened to think of it.

You're sometimes unwilling to admit your ignorance ...

'It's – I wondered – It's only – Rabbit,
I suppose you don't know.
What does the North Pole look like?'
'Well,' said Rabbit, stroking his whiskers,
'now you're asking me.'
'I did know once, only I've sort of forgotten,'
said Christopher Robin carelessly.
'It's a funny thing,' said Rabbit, 'but I've sort
of forgotten too, although I did know once.'

... AND MAY NOT KNOW MUCH ABOUT THE WORLD.

'There's a South Pole,'
said Christopher Robin,
'and I expect there's an East Pole
and a West Pole, though people
don't like talking about them.'

You can't teach those who won't listen.

'Pooh,' said Piglet reproachfully, 'haven't you been listening to what Rabbit was saying?'
'I listened, but I had a small piece of fluff in my ear. Could you say it again, please, Rabbit?'

You value those who know what's important to you.

'Thank you, Christopher Robin.
You're the only one who seems to
understand about tails.
They don't think – that's what's the
matter with some of these others.
They've no imagination.
A tail isn't a tail to them, it's just a
Little Bit Extra at the back.'

BUT ULTIMATELY, IT'S REASSURING TO KNOW THAT EVERYONE GETS CONFUSED SOMETIMES.

'Hallo, Piglet,' he said. 'I thought you were out.'
'No,' said Piglet, 'it's you who were out, Pooh.'
'So it was,' said Pooh. 'I knew one of us was.'

ABOUT A.A.MILNE

A.A.Milne was born in London in 1882. He began writing as a contributor to *Punch* magazine, and also wrote plays and poetry. Winnie-the-Pooh made his first appearance in *Punch* magazine in 1923. Soon after, in 1926, Milne published his first stories about Winnie-the-Pooh, which were an instant success. Since then, Pooh has become a world-famous bear, and Milne's stories have been translated into approximately forty different languages.

ABOUT E.H.SHEPARD

E.H.Shepard was born in London in 1879. He won a scholarship to the Royal Academy Schools and later, like Milne, worked for *Punch* magazine, as a cartoonist and illustrator. Shepard's witty and loving illustrations of Winnie~the~Pooh and his friends in the Hundred Acre Wood have become an inseparable part of the Pooh stories, and his illustrations have become classics in their own right.

COLLECT ALL FOUR BOOKS

WINNIE-THE-POOH
GLOOM & DOOM
FOR PESSIMISTS

A.A.MILNE
with decorations by E.H.SHEPARD

WINNIE-THE-POOH
DOUBT & DISQUIET
FOR WORRIERS

A.A.MILNE
with decorations by E.H.SHEPARD

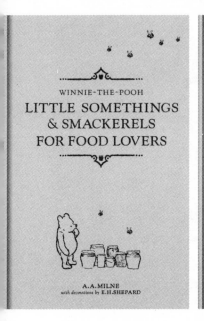

WINNIE-THE-POOH

LITTLE SOMETHINGS & SMACKERELS FOR FOOD LOVERS

A.A.MILNE
with decorations by E.H.SHEPARD

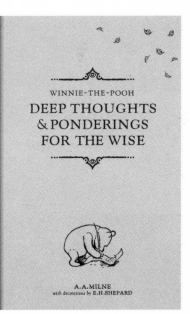

WINNIE-THE-POOH

DEEP THOUGHTS & PONDERINGS FOR THE WISE

A.A.MILNE
with decorations by E.H.SHEPARD

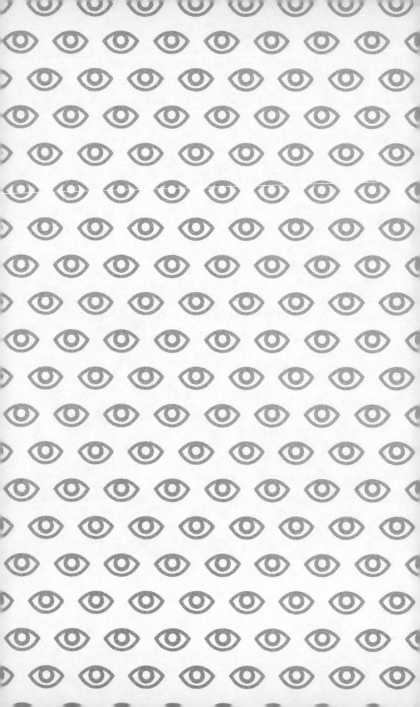